SAVING
YOUR SKIN

ANNE HUNT

Edited by Eric Mein, M.D.

ARE
PRESS

ASSOCIATION FOR
RESEARCH AND
ENLIGHTENMENT

A.R.E. Press • Virginia Beach • Virginia

A Note to the Reader

The information in this book is not presented as prescription for the treatment of disease. Application of the medical information found in the Edgar Cayce readings and interpreted herein should be undertaken only under the supervision of a physician.

Other Books in This Series

WEIGHT NO MORE: A Weight-Loss Program That Can Work
WINNING THE COLD WAR: Preventing and Curing
the Common Cold and Flu

Cover illustration by Cynthia Fisher

Table of Contents

If we would have life, give it. If we would have love, make ourselves lovely. If we would have beauty within our lives, make our lives beautiful. **Based on reading 2096-1**

EDGAR CAYCE
PIONEER IN HOLISTIC HEALTH CARE

PREFACE

It's no secret that our society is in the midst of a health care crisis. The problem is partly economic, as we struggle to find ways to pay for the high level of care made possible by medical technology. It's also a research crisis, as scientists look for cures to new diseases such as AIDS. Those are the sorts of problems that make the headlines. Those are the challenges that are clearly evident.

But our health care crisis has more subtle features, too—aspects that are easy to miss but just as important. For example, how much guarantee can doctors give us for our health? How much responsibility are we willing to accept *for ourselves?* Are there some ailments for which *self-care* is not only more economical but also more likely to produce the results we want?

Another elusive feature of our society's health care crisis is in our attitude toward health and healing itself. Recent decades have seen an explosion of alternative health services, many of them claiming to follow a more natural or a more holistic approach. The success of some of these new methods makes us wonder about the validity of the familiar medical model. Is the body really more or less a machine that gets fixed like a balky appliance or a malfunctioning vehicle? Or is the human being a rich, complex mixture of body, mind, and spirit where problems at one level must be addressed at all three?

Working in the first four-and-a-half decades of the twentieth century, Edgar Cayce was a tremendous resource that we can now draw upon to meet the modern crisis in health care. His approach and methods for health maintenance and healing feature self-care that is often, yet not always, in conjunction with a physician's guidance. He was truly a pioneer of the contemporary holistic health movement and ahead of his times in pointing out the attitudinal, emotional, and spiritual components of disease.

Although best known as a "psychic" (or "the sleeping prophet," referring to his occasional predictions about world conditions), Cayce might be better labeled as a "clairvoyant diagnostician" or an "intuitive physician." The point with these descriptive terms is to emphasize first that Cayce's work was principally diagnostic and prescriptive. He was not a healer nor did he have office hours to see patients the way a doctor would. The people who came to him for help were almost invariably those who had unsuccessfully tried the traditional medical approaches of their day and came to Cayce as a last resort, asking "What's *really* wrong with me? What treatments— no matter how unusual—will bring relief and healing?"

But as the descriptive labels for Cayce also

emphasize, his method of meeting those requests was intuitive. He had no formal medical school training. Yet he was apparently able to alter his consciousness in such a way that he could see clairvoyantly the real origins of afflictions (physical, mental, and spiritual). What's more, he could then prescribe natural and holistic treatment procedures—sometimes requiring the involvement of a physician or other health care professional, but often needing only a self-care regimen.

The material came through as lengthy discourses (called "readings"), which were stenographically recorded and then transcribed. Most of the information was given for specific individuals and their afflictions, but on occasion there were readings given on particular health topics which contained universally applicable information.

This book is one of a series of volumes in which common ailments and health difficulties are directed. Each topic addresses information given by Cayce which is principally focused upon self-care. The author, Anne Hunt, has carefully researched those readings on the respective health concern, focusing on the treatment procedures that were suggested to many different people as well as those recommendations that were clearly indicated for general use. Her research compilation and writing go a long way toward making these helpful methods accessible to us all. You'll find all the books in this series highly readable and very practical.

Anne's collaborator is Dr. Eric Mein, who served as medical editor. Sometimes Cayce's language requires the insight of a trained physician to translate concepts into modern terminology. Often there are new findings in medical research that shed light on one of Cayce's ideas. Eric has skillfully added that dimension to the creation of this book.

This particular volume in the series focuses on care of the skin, something that should concern all of us, not just those preoccupied with appearances. The skin is an extraordinary organ. Like every essential organ, it needs to be respected, nurtured, and allowed to best perform its vital tasks. The Cayce readings are full of insights about natural, holistic methods for skin care—ones that allow both our inner and outer beauty to shine through. They offer a highly practical, self-care approach to healthy skin and hair.

Mark Thurston, Ph.D.
Association for Research and Enlightenment, Inc.

INTRODUCTION

Our skin is a wonderful example of just how remarkable our bodies are. Cited by dermatologists as the largest organ of the body, the skin has a surface area averaging 1.5 to 2.0 square meters and, combined with its deeper layers, can weigh up to 40 pounds. Far more than an inert wrapping, this "organ" serves as the main interface between our bodies and the environment. Its complex structure is capable of many tasks, including providing sensory information, physical and chemical protection, and temperature control. The skin's tough flexibility allows us the capacity to perform not only rough manual labor but also finer more delicate tasks and allows us the use of subtle gestures and expressions for communication. Its two to four million eccrine glands, which combined have the mass of a kidney, can perspire up to several liters in one hour and ten liters in a day. Finally, it has a great capacity for rapid regeneration.

This "organ" is always readily available for our inspection and often catches our attention. Disorders of the skin itself account for a substantial portion of medical care, and a family physician may see up to 20% of his or her patients for dermatologic complaints. This attention is justified, as the skin often mirrors activity of the body's internal organs. It can also respond to external influences ranging from humidity to more serious problems, such as toxic chemicals and ionizing radiation. This ready availability also places the skin in a unique position to receive from us extra care and attention to detail.

The skin also illustrates the role the mind can play in health. Certain mood alterations are clearly reflected by the skin in the form of blushing or blanching or perspiration. A conclusive relationship between emotions and skin disease is not quite as clear and remains the subject of current debate. However, physician-author Lewis Thomas writes that the extensive evidence showing that warts respond to suggestion alone is "more of a surprise than cloning, recombinant DNA or endorphins or acupuncture . . . It illustrates there has to be a Person in charge, running matters of meticulous detail beyond anyone's comprehension, a skilled engineer and manager, a chief executive—and a world-class cell biologist."

Fifty years ago, information from another source—the psychic readings of Edgar Cayce—invited its listeners to use "mental forces" to eradicate warts. The holistic approach to the skin and hair that you'll find within the pages of this book comes from that source. One of the foremost psychics of the twentieth century, Cayce gave the majority of his readings to individuals with health concerns who sought his advice. The readings clearly saw the skin as an important organ of elimination, and their approach to caring for the skin and treating its disorders reflects this.

These readings invite us to put this information to the test in our own lives. There is no better place to start this than with skin and hair care. The suggestions are usually simple and easy, and the results clearly visible for our own scrutiny. Enjoy this book and use the information it contains on your journey to better health.

Eric A. Mein, M.D.
Meridian Institute

Chapter 1

BEAUTY IS MORE THAN SKIN DEEP

BEAUTY IS WITHIN

Helen of Troy. A name synonymous with beauty. The face which launched a thousand ships. From somewhere deep inside, Helen's beauty radiated outward to capture the imagination—first of Greeks, then of Trojans, and finally of the world. This same beauty is deep within each of us. Though we may not aspire to stir nations to arms, we *do* want to look, feel, and be our best.

We can each evoke our own natural beauty by caring for our bodies in ways that they will then care for our skin. If we view our bodies as perfectly designed vehicles for our souls—which have marvelous powers to live, heal, and grow—then we are inspired to give them the assistance they need to maintain balance and health. Our success will be reflected in a healthy, radiant glow that comes from deep within.

The Edgar Cayce readings indicated that we are each entrusted with our bodies at birth and that we should gently care for and nurture them throughout our lives. Our purpose for striving for health and beauty should be a desire to add beauty and be of service to the world in which we live. Whether we are planning a diet or receiving a massage, it's good to keep this simple truth in mind.

To care properly for our bodies we must be grounded in a basic understanding of how they work and what support they need on a day-to-day basis. Since care for skin and hair is our focus, we must learn how they are constructed and what body systems lend them support.

GETTING UNDER YOUR SKIN

Although we often primp and pamper, we take the greater purposes of our skin for granted. If asked to list our body's vital organs, we would begin: "heart, liver, kidneys, etc." Somewhere on the list we might correctly include the skin, though perhaps we'd be a bit unsure whether or not we were right to do so. But the fact is that the skin is our body's largest organ, covering seventeen square feet on the average adult. Not only does it reflect our beauty and define our image, it also protects our inner organs, regulates our temperature, and assists in the elimination of fluids and toxins. Our outer mantle is self creating, replacing itself with new cells roughly once a month. Though we do not shed our skins in the same way as some reptiles do, we are constantly washing away dead skin and generating new skin in its place.

2

In simple terms, the skin is made up of three layers: the epidermis, the dermis, and the subcutaneous tissue.

The epidermis, or outer layer, consists of four sublayers. Outermost is the stratum corneum which, along with the barrier level just beneath it, serves to protect the skin from harmful elements. Growing and maturing cells come next, with the cell nursery being the bottommost sublayer of the epidermis. Here new cells are generated and from here they begin their upward journey to view, if ever so briefly, the light of day. It's important to note that the epidermis does not contain any blood vessels and thus relies upon the second layer of skin for nutritional support.

This second layer of supportive skin is the dermis, which is three or four times thicker than its upstairs neighbor. It is an important layer whose health and vitality greatly affects our outer appearance. Capillary blood vessels, nerves, fibrous or elastic tissues, hair follicles, sweat glands, and sebaceous or oil glands call this layer home. Here you'll also find your beauty allies: collagen and elastin. These last two substances give your skin its resiliency and ward off the sags and bags of age *and* abuse.

Supporting this "dermis duo" is the subcutaneous or fatty layer, which both cushions our skin and provides insulation for the body. It is connected to the muscles below by fibrous tissues. Nurturing this connective tissue with gentle care, being sure not to tug and pull at the skin as you wash, dry, and moisturize, will also contribute to a firm and smooth complexion.

SKIN TYPES

To treat the skin properly, it is helpful to understand the three basic skin types: dry, oily, and normal.

Dry skin is the most common type, especially as we age. Its flakiness and redness are compounded by the tight, itchy feeling which worsens during the cold, blustery months. Even your entire body can be affected: Hands may get chapped, legs irritated, and the stomach area, where waist bands may stunt circulation, can burn and itch.

Oily skin is less common but prone to more surface problems, such as acne and other blemishes, particularly in the facial area. Enlarged pores and blackheads add to the difficulties. Often associated with adolescence, oily skin can have as emotional an impact on an adult as on a sixteen-year-old. It can be unsightly, potentially scaring, and much more damaging to self-image than dry, itchy skin.

Normal skin over the entire body is, as you would probably imagine, quite rare. Most people, however, do have normal skin on at least some portion of their bodies. This type of skin is soft and moist with few if any enlarged pores and tends to be clear and even in color and texture. If you're lucky enough to have this category of skin, remember one thing: Age, weather, diet, and any other number of elements can change it, so guard its life with your health!

As you may have realized, a combination of these skin types can and does often occur. Your entire body may even have patches of all three skin types and pose a particular challenge in treatment and care. For instance, dry skin may plague your hands while oily pores populate your forehead. Yet, the rest of your body may be quite normal. With time, as you learn how to vitalize your skin from within, this irregular skin condition can be healed effectively.

CROWNING GLORY

Your hair is made up of 97% protein and 3% other minerals and ash. Each strand of your sometimes tangled tresses grows from a hair follicle which is located in the dermis layer of your skin. In the follicle itself is a sebaceous gland which produces an oil called sebum. In balanced quantity this oil helps condition and protect the hair, keeping it pliable and strong.

Microscopic blood vessels deliver a stream of nutrients important to the health of the follicle. As your hair grows, it leaves behind cells, almost like seeds, which later form a new strand of hair when the old one falls out. Baldness and permanent loss of hair occurs if new cells are not deposited and properly nourished.

MOVING ON TO HEALTHIER SKIN AND HAIR

Now that you know a little about the makeup of the functional facade with which you greet the world—your skin and hair—you're ready for practical advice on how to assure their health and beauty. The following chapters offer you just that. Not only will you learn a great deal about preventative maintenance, you'll also find helpful, holistic advice for specific skin and hair ailments.

Chapter 2

THE WINNING SKIN INNER WORKOUT

BEGIN WITHIN

Since we know that beauty begins within, it is important to know exactly where and how its creation occurs. The Cayce readings revealed a half dozen "inner allies" which can be called to duty in your campaign for healthier skin and hair. These are:

- Diet
- Eliminations
- Circulation
- Thryoid
- Spine
- Relaxation

TOP TWO

Of the items on this list, diet and eliminations stand out as a strong foundation upon which to build your strategy for a healthier, more vital outward glow. Begin by getting these two areas of your life and health in the best shape possible. Although they can't be corrected and perfected overnight, you can begin today to take steps toward their improvement by following the suggestions in this chapter.

YOU ARE WHAT YOU EAT

Diet, nutrition, and assimilation. Hundreds of Cayce readings chanted this refrain, many in relation to the health of skin and hair. Below is a version of the renowned Cayce diet which will promote healthy skin and hair. Pay special attention to the "Super Skin and Hair Friends" and include these foods in your diet on a regular basis. Remember, though, not to overdo any one food item. The body thrives on balance and variety in its diet. That's why the world is such a marvelous cornucopia of healthy, edible, natural foods!

SUPER SKIN AND HEALTHY HAIR DIET

80% OF YOUR DIET

- Fruits
- Vegetables
- Almonds, chestnuts, Brazil nuts, and hazelnuts
- Eight glasses of pure spring water
- Herbal teas

- Whole grain breads
- Dairy products
- Fish, fowl, and lamb (lean)
- Whole grain cereals, bran, and wheat germ
- Peanuts, pecans, and walnuts

SUPER SKIN AND HAIR FRIENDS

- Seafood and kelp for their iodine content
- Sunflower seeds, soybeans, cheese, milk, and green vegetables for their high calcium content
- Vegetable juices, especially those containing lettuce, carrots, and celery to strengthen the nerve forces which help keep the body regulated and balanced
- Two almonds a day for prevention of acne
- Orange juice with lemon once a day, preferably before retiring, to help alkalinize the system
- Liver, carrots, and green and yellow vegetables for their vitamin A content

SUPER SKIN AND HAIR ENEMIES

- Red meats and pork
- Animal fats
- Sweets
- Fried foods
- White bread

All of these high-fat content foods hamper proper assimilation and elimination.

- Excessive quantities of cabbage which inhibit the assimilation of iodine

CLOSE-UP ON NUTRITION

It's obvious from the list of "Super Skin and Hair Friends" that certain vitamins and minerals are beneficial for the skin and hair. Below is an explanation of them and their properties relative to this topic.

Iodine. Iodine is critical to a healthy thyroid. Cayce indicated that a healthy thyroid can mean healthy skin and hair. Nutritionists are in agreement with Cayce; both concur that this mineral promotes healthy nails and teeth as well.

Calcium. Cayce pinpointed calcium as being important to the health of skin and hair. Although he offers no explanation for this suggestion, it's possible that he is zeroing in on an important role of calcium—its role in facilitating nerve impulse transmission. The nervous system is vital in regulating the body's circulatory system, which is vital to the health of skin and hair. Like iodine, calcium also befriends your teeth and nails.

Vitamin A. Nutritionists and dermatologists alike tout the benefits of vitamin A in the treatment of skin and hair problems and the general maintenance of a healthy outer look. Also, vitamin A is necessary for the body to synthesize protein, which is important to healthy hair. Cayce linked vitamin A, as he did calcium, with health of the nerve forces within the body which regulate and control our every function.

VITAMIN SUPPLEMENTS

Should you take supplements? Cayce invariably recommended that the best source of any and all vitamins and minerals is from natural foods. In one reading he stated that iodine and calcium "will be the more helpful if they are assimilated from foods than by the administration in any other manners." And he added, " . . . the helpful influence passes then through the entire activity of the assimilating and distributing of energies, *by* that assimilation through the body." (Edgar Cayce reading 619-10)[1]

The readings mentioned two additional cautions. First, taking vitamins *continuously* can affect the body's ability to assimilate them from natural sources. Supplements can make your body lazy in its efforts to extract the vitamins from your food intake. Second, if you provide the body with excessive nutrients, you force it to deal with the excess amount as a waste, adding more work to your elimination systems.

However, in special instances where there was a depletion of vital energies due to a deficiency, vitamin supplements were recommended. Should you feel the need to take a vitamin supplement, consult with your physician or pharmacist. Then, follow the readings' recommendation that supplements be taken in cycles. One good routine is to take the particular vitamin for two weeks, then discontinue for one week. Follow this cycle until you feel that your diet and assimilation processes

---

[1]The Edgar Cayce readings have each been assigned a two-part number for identification. The first digits indicate the specific number assigned to the topic or individual obtaining the reading. Since many received more than one reading, the second set of digits following the hyphen indicates the number in that particular series of readings.

have improved enough to provide you with vitamins and minerals from natural sources.

ASSIMILATION

As hinted at previously, without proper assimilation the healthiest foods in the world can pass through your body unnoticed and underutilized. It's a fact of life many don't recognize, and few understand.

Assimilation is how you digest, absorb, and use the foods you consume. If there are conditions in your body which prevent proper processing, then the best diet in the world won't bring about the healthy hair and smooth skin you both desire and deserve.

Assimilation begins with your eating patterns and habits.

FOOD COMBINING

Food combining is a simple practice which can have powerful results. The fact is that some foods are friendly with one another, others are natural enemies. In more technical terms, mixing different food types results in particular chemical reactions, some of which are positive for the body, others of which are not. Eating such warring foods can result in adverse effects on the digestive process and greatly disturb any hope of proper assimilation.

Here are some basic guidelines to help you combine your foods correctly:

FOOD-COMBINING CHART

Food Type	Agrees	Disagrees
Starches	Vegetables	Milk, fruits, eggs, cheese, nuts, meats, sweets
Meats, seafood, fowl, nuts	Vegetables	Starches, milk, fruits, sweets, cheese
Vegetables	All foods	
Dairy	Vegetables, fruits	Starches, meats, fish, fowl
Fruits (sweet)	Vegetables, dairy	Meats, fowl, seafood, eggs
Fruits (tart)	Vegetables	Starches, milk

SECRET SUBSTANCE

The Cayce readings offered a helpful, easy hint to assist the body in assimilation. They suggested including unflavored, natural gelatin in your diet to aid your body in the absorption of nutrients, especially vitamins. A fruit salad prepared with gelatin or the mixing of gelatin with fresh fruit juices are excellent additions to your daily fare. What makes this work? It's simple. Gelatin acts as an enzyme in the body and assists in the digestion and the routing of nutrients. So take this simple advice. Purchase pure gelatin at your grocery store and sprinkle it on your salads or add it to your fruit juice. It is a tasteless, powerful medicine you'll find easy to take.

EAT SLOWLY AND WITH A THANKFUL ATTITUDE

Taking a moment to bless the food we eat and the companionship we often share at mealtime is a tradition in cultures around the world. This moment of rest and awareness of our blessings can have a very positive effect upon our body's reception of the foods we eat. On many occasions Cayce warned against eating while under stress or when angry. If you've ever eaten when in this condition and found the result to be a case of indigestion, you know that Cayce was right.

In addition to your daily routine of a thankful moment before eating, make a commitment to eat slowly, chew your food thoroughly and thoughtfully, and maintain a conscious, grateful attitude all during the meal. For good measure, visualize the healthful effects of your food while you are eating, and you'll be surprised at the rewards.

YOU BECOME WHAT YOU KEEP

Cayce painted a fairly vivid picture of how poor eliminations set off a chain reaction which results in many body imbalances, including unhealthy skin and possible hair loss. In basic terms, if the body does not expel wastes, there is a toxic build-up which results in poor coordination between the deeper superficial circulations. This results in an additional toxic build-up in the capillaries, further hindering circulation. Since superficial circulation supplies nourishment to the dermis and epidermis layers of the skin, a breakdown in this system can cause serious skin problems.

In the course of a day, your body is involved in many processes which produce waste byproducts. Of course, you're aware that as your body digests food, wastes are created which must be eliminated. Add to this the two types of waste which are created at the cellular level. There are wastes created when living cells burn energy, and there are billions of dying cells as well which add to the internal pollution problem. Top these off with the carbon dioxide from the body's use of oxygen and your body's tremendous need for waste disposal becomes evident.

The human body, though, is well designed to care for its needs. If all is in order—*and that's the challenge*—the body can dispose of its wastes efficiently and effectively.

What organs need to be in order? Your colon, kidneys and liver, skin and lungs. Here's some good advice that will help keep these systems properly functioning.

WATER

Drink eight glasses of water a day, starting off the morning with a half glass of warm water to aid in the cleansing process. Water will benefit all elimination systems, even the lungs and especially the skin. Remember that the skin is an open sieve. Water is needed to wash away the toxins which build up in the dermis

14

layer. Natural spring or mineral water is highly recommended. The following routine will help you remember when to head to the watering hole:

Schedule	Count
Upon arising (warm water)	½ glass
Mid-morning and afternoon	2
Just before breakfast, lunch, and dinner	3
Right after breakfast, lunch, and dinner	3
Total	8½

After one week of this routine, you'll be amazed at how your body responds. If you forget a glass in your routine, you'll find that your body will sound the water alarm. You'll begin to drink of the water of life automatically.

There's also an added benefit. You'll find that the water routine not only supplies you with energy but helps balance your energy throughout the day.

FIBER

Consume a high-fiber diet which includes plenty of raw vegetables and a balanced quantity of whole grains. One simple suggestion which you should follow is to eat a raw vegetable lunch. In doing this, follow an additional suggestion from the Cayce readings: Combine three vegetables that grow above the ground to one that grows below the ground when you prepare your fresh, cleansing lunch.

Also, eat a comfortable quantity of natural laxatives, such as figs, prunes, dates, and raisins. They make healthy and tasty snack foods—and are imminently more advantageous to your skin than potato chips.

LAXATIVES

You may occasionally feel the need to take a mild laxative. Recommended in the readings were two which you should keep in your home medicine chest. Here's what they are and how to take them:

Castoria Castoria is a mild laxative recommended in almost 150 readings. It is derived from senna which originates from a plant. Many different dosages were recommended, though the average adult dosage was a half teaspoon every hour. Continue taking this medicine until you have had one or more bowel movements and you feel that your alimentary canal has fully responded. This routine usually takes a full day during which you should also rest.

Eno Salts Eno salts is another frequently recommended laxative, appearing in over 180 readings. It is a substance derived from fruit salts. A standard dosage is one teaspoon in the morning for five mornings, discontinue for five days, and then repeat. Do this until you feel that your bowels are regulated and cleansed.

COLONICS AND ENEMAS

Even if your bowel movements feel regular and consistent and you occasionally use a laxative to cleanse your system, you still might want to visit a health-care professional twice a year for a colonic. A periodic internal cleansing of the colon makes sense. No matter how fibrous your diet or how consistent you are in your intake of water, there will be a build-up of wastes clinging to the walls and hiding in the folds of the colon. This layer of film and deposits can inhibit the colon's ability to absorb and process nutrients from the foods you eat.

What if you can't locate a practitioner to give you a colonic? Then administer an enema to yourself at home, perhaps on a more frequent basis. Though a colonic is as effective as four to six enemas, an internal cleansing of either kind, carefully administered, will have tremendous effects on your health. For instructions on how to administer an enema, refer to Appendix D.

STEAMING CLEAN

Perspiration in general is an important elimination process and has particular benefit to the skin. The best way of obtaining a good sweat is from a steam cabinet or sauna in a health facility that provides this service. Many massage therapists, for instance, will have a cabinet available so that you can take a steam before your massage. Also, you may belong to a health club with a steam room. If you do, don't overlook the benefit of a good sweat for five to ten minutes following your workout.

But steams aren't relegated to only the fortunate few who have access to such facilities. Hydrotherapy can also be administered at home following the directions below. The first time you set one up may seem involved, but once you have the routine down, it will be quite an easy process and one that you will enjoy. You should attempt to find time for a steam about twice a month. For instructions on how to set up a homemade steam cabinet, refer to Appendix D.

RETREAT TO THE TUB

Don't overlook the therapeutic benefits of a nice, hot bath which makes you lightly perspire. Try to retreat to the tub three to four times a week when the house is calm and quiet. Take your soap (Castile, olive-oil based, or Black and White), natural sea sponge, and peanut oil with you.

Soak for fifteen to twenty minutes in the clear, clean water. Then, sponge with soap to invigorate your body. Finish your bath and turn on the shower and rinse in warm water. Now, rub your body with pure peanut oil, Peanut Oil Lotion or Olive Oil Skin Freshener (see Chapter 4). Wrap up in a soft robe, and relax for at least a half hour.

Make this a lifelong ritual several times a week, and you'll add years to your life and your skin!

FRESH AIR AND DEEP BREATHING

It's quite possible that our lungs are the most abused and ignored organs of the elimination systems. Why?

Most of us take the breathing process for granted and don't realize that lungs do more than provide us with life-giving oxygen—they help us expel life-threatening carbon dioxide along with other toxic gases from our bodies. We are virtually oblivious to our breathing patterns. Compounded by the effects of the pollution in the air we breathe, we may be in more trouble than we realize!

Become conscious of your breathing patterns. Try to make your breaths deep and regular. Also, exercise regularly out of doors when possible. There are several specific exercises described in the next chapter which not only stimulate circulation, but also promote deep breathing and the expelling of toxic gases.

Chapter 3

FINE-TUNING YOUR MACHINE

FINAL FOUR

Once you have taken steps toward the improvement of the "top two" inner allies (diet and eliminations), it's time to fine-tune other vital systems within your body which also directly affect the health of your skin and hair. They are the "final four": circulation, thyroid, spine, and relaxation.

RIVERS OF LIFE

There are two circulatory systems which are vital to your body's health: the blood system and the lymphatic system. The Cayce readings indicate that these two systems work as a team. The blood's primary function is to deliver nutrients and oxygen throughout the body with an additional function of carrying out wastes. The lymph also plays a major role in the elimination of wastes. Without its vital assistance in this area, the blood system would be inadequate.

In understanding the importance of stimulating these two systems so that they work at their optimum level, it is necessary to realize how the two differ. The power behind the blood flow is generated by an efficiently designed pump—the heart. The lymphatic system, however, has no pump. It relies on the body's general activity level to supply it with the pressures and stimulation to move the fluid through the body. Massage, exercise, and spinal adjustments can stimulate the blood circulation on the one hand and literally generate the lymphatic flow on the other.

BEING RUBBED THE RIGHT WAY

According to Dr. Harold J. Reilly, author of *The Edgar Cayce Handbook for Health Through Drugless Therapy*, an hourlong massage can have as equal a benefit to the body as four hours of restful sleep. It's a therapy you should include as a regular part of your schedule. Massage has long since graduated from the parlors and is now a recognized health-care practice. Simply find a massage therapist with whom you feel comfortable and stick with the regular treatment. Have a massage at least twice a month or weekly, if possible.

Suggest that your therapist use peanut oil for your massages, if you are particularly concerned about the health of your skin. According to Cayce, this oil serves as a nutrient to the skin and muscles and makes them more pliable. Resilience is important in warding off sags and bags.

Don't overlook the benefits of self-massage. It's a good idea to rub your body down with peanut oil, kneading the muscles and lubricating the joints. Every day!

KEEPING FIT FOR FABULOUS SKIN

Exercise is vital in stimulating circulation. If you don't keep moving, your blood and lymph will slow down accordingly. Cayce gave a general recommendation to exercise the upper body in the morning, the lower body at night. Keep this in mind as you design your own, personal exercise routine.

Below are a few special exercises to incorporate into your daily routine. Though you will want to supplement them with other exercises with which you are familiar and comfortable, these have particular benefits to those body systems which affect skin and hair.

Morning Breathing Exercise This exercise will help get your lymph flowing after you've been rather inactive for much of the night. The leg-tightening involved in this exercise acts to pump the lymph into motion via muscle action. Also, there is a lymph "cistern" at the level of the diaphragm which is massaged during this deep-breathing exercise.

In the morning we are in particular need of a good dose of oxygen because our breathing, while we were asleep, was light and shallow. We need to pump up our lungs and expel toxins that may have accumulated during the night as our body, too, slept.

Upon arising, stand in front of an open window (when the air outside, we hope, is fresh!) and breathe deeply, gradually raising your hands and arms above your head. At the same time, with a flowing motion, rise up on your toes, then tighten your leg muscles and bend forward from the hips (this takes balance and practice!). Exhale through the nose as you bend over. After your lungs are empty, inhale through the mouth and straighten up. Repeat for five to six minutes. Then continue with your breathing by closing first your right nostril with your right forefinger, raise your left arm, and breathe in deeply through the left nostril. Exhale through the mouth and lower your arm. Repeat in the same way, this time closing your left nostril and breathing in deeply through your right, raising your right arm. Then exhale through the mouth and lower your arm.

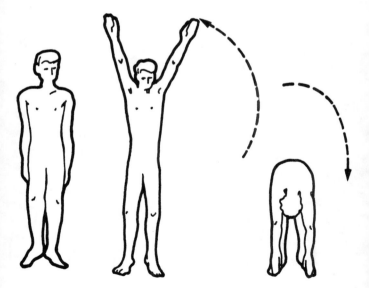

23

A minimum amount of physical activity is not the only enemy of the circulatory sytems. Poorly functioning elimination systems can also affect these rivers of life. When toxins build up, circulation is paralyzed. It's as though the toxins, which can form in pockets throughout your bodily tissues, set up roadblocks to hinder the blood and lymph. This happens especially in the superficial circulation, which is necessary to the health of the dermis, where hair follicles, sweat glands, collagen, and elastin—all vital to healthy, resilient hair and skin—reside.

Both the steam and hot baths previously described will stimulate circulation. But three other therapies will also give your circulation an added boost. These are: massage, exercise, and osteopathic adjustments. Let's now look at a few more helpful exercises.

Head and Neck   This exercise was recommended in the Cayce readings over 300 times. Because it helps stimulate circulation throughout the neck, head, face, and scalp, it is particularly beneficial.

Sit with your spine erect and your shoulders relaxed. Bend your head forward three times, backward three times, to the right three times, to the left three times. Then, gently rotate your head 360° in both directions three times. Do this series slowly and deliberately, morning, noon, and night.

24

Pelvic Roll The following exercise, to be included in your evening routine, was recommended by Cayce to stimulate glandular activity.

Position yourself on your stomach as if preparing to do a pushup, but with your feet against a wall. Elevate yourself on your hands, then rotate your hips in a circle—three times clockwise, three times counterclockwise. Ideally, keep your elbows straight while you execute this exercise. However, if it is too strenuous, you may actually rest on your elbows rather than your hands when you assume the pushup position.

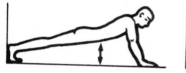 

Overhead Swing A special exercise was given for those with dry hands and skin. The readings indicated that this simple exercise would aid in assimilating nutrients in the body. Stretch the arms above the head and reach as high as you can or, even better, grab hold of a bar or other structure that you can safely swing from (the readings suggested a tree limb!). Hold on, relaxing your body, not your grip! Stretch or swing like this until you feel the tension leave your body. Repeat regularly once or twice a day.

Walking This is a frequently recommended general exercise which accomplishes several goals. It exercises muscles which helps open dormant capillaries, massaging them in a way that pumps the blood through the extremities. And, of course, it stimulates the lymph and helps get toxins moving along to the eliminating organs. The fresh air you breathe while walking also benefits the lungs while the light sweat cleanses the skin.

An ideal routine is to take a walk in the morning after a healthy breakfast and again in the evening after a light, well-rounded dinner. Swing your arms and breathe deeply as you walk along. Because of your schedule, you may have to settle for just one walk a day. If so, it's best to fit it into your schedule at a time when you can relax and be at peace.

FINAL WORD ON EXERCISE

The Cayce readings stressed that the best exercises are the ones you do! Remember this statement as you plan your day. Make your exercise time as important as the time you sleep and eat. Your body has specific needs for these activities and will not be at its best if one of them is missing. The readings even added that irregular exercise can be as harmful as none at all, probably because there is more chance of overdoing it if we are unaccustomed to this kind of activity. Remember this hint when tempted to skip your exercise period for something which seems more appealing. Make the healthy choice—exercise!

THYROID FACTOR

How does the thyroid fit into the picture?

Your thyroid gland is located just in front of the windpipe at the base of the throat. When the thyroid gland is mentioned, everyone immediately thinks of its role in regulating metabolism and growth. Cayce connected metabolism with the proper functioning of the nervous system, helping to stimulate eliminations and circulation, both of which are important to healthy skin and hair.

As mentioned previously, Cayce was also in agreement with medical researchers in stating that a large portion of the body's iodine is stored in the thyroid and that this gland plays a key role in healthy skin, hair, nails, and teeth. There's great wisdom, then, in keeping this gland properly balanced.

Poor thyroid functioning is a recurrent theme in many of the readings on skin conditions. The following therapy can be used as a standard regimen for stimulating the thyroid's activity. You should do this routine once every three or four months to keep all the glands clear and functioning.

THYROID THERAPY

Atomidine (iodine trichloride) can be taken in cyclic doses to help stimulate the glandular system. Cayce pinpointed Atomidine specifically for this therapy because it is less toxic than regular forms of iodine. A standard routine is to begin with 1 drop in half a glass of water in the morning. The next morning take 2 drops, and 3 drops the following morning. On the fourth day go back down to 2 drops, and on the fifth, 1 drop. Repeat this 5-day cycle once every 28 days.

Remember, too, to eat foods rich in iodine and calcium as a part of your regular diet—though don't overdo!

Finally, when applying lotions and mud packs (described in Chapter 4), remember to massage these compounds not only on the face but over the neck and thyroid area as well. Your thyroid will respond positively to being noticed.

VITAL CIRCUITS

Your spine is the central communication network of your nervous system. Simply stated, the brain sends signals down the spinal cord, which are then relayed to their destination through a complex communications system for which the spine functions as the "trunk line." Over 10 billion neurons make up these vital circuits.

Nerve impulses thus serve many functions. Their most basic one is to nurture all the cells within the body. Nerves stimulate growth, development, and self-maintenance on a cellular level. On a larger scale, they regulate the activities of the organs and glands, controlling their blood supply.

Cayce targeted spinal misalignments (called "subluxations") in many readings on complexion and hair-loss problems. In the event of a "short circuit" in the spine, nerve impulses can become misdirected or weak. Short circuits can then occur throughout the network, wreaking havoc. Where skin problems and hair loss result, it's possible that the spinal misalignment had an adverse effect on circulation or distribution of vital energies into the epidermis layer of the skin. Or, the initial victim may have been the thyroid which, like other glands, depends on nerve impulses to function properly.

It's not possible to suggest specific spinal misalignments which have adverse effects on the skin and hair. This subject is complex and the area must be diagnosed and treated by a medical professional. The best route to follow is to have a regular adjustment, perhaps every other week, by an osteopath or chiropractor. If you have specific health concerns, discuss those prior to the adjustment.

REST AND RELAXATION

You already know that lack of required sleep shows first on your face. However, you need to realize that lack of those nocturnal hours also takes a toll on your skin and hair, from head to foot. So your glance in the mirror only tells a portion of the story.

Sleep provides your body and its billions of cells with an opportunity for repair, recuperation, and rejuvenation. The readings stated clearly that "The body rebuilds faster asleep than awake, because we have not the wear of the mind on the whole system." (Edgar Cayce reading 3919-2) Without this time in the shop, cells begin to sag and droop with fatigue. Your circulation becomes sluggish, toxins build up, and your limbs become heavy.

The best sleep schedule is the one that your body calls out for naturally. Eight hours is considered the average time required for sleep, though this will vary in individuals. The best advice is to fall into the natural rhythm of your body and be consistent in the amount of time you afford it for sleep.

RELAXATION

Relaxation is best described as that time away from the cares and stresses of your everyday routine. Some of the most powerful elements of your psyche are your attitudes and emotions. If, during the day, you have a disturbing argument or hear some upsetting news, you've fueled your body with degenerative "nerve impulses" that can adversely affect your health. For centuries humanity has recognized the effect of emotions on health. When we are happy and content, our bodies tend to feel more vital and full of energy. On the other hand, if we experience a saddening loss, we are sapped of energy and often feel nauseous and achy.

The most important step in taming emotions is to recognize what emotions we are feeling. This is not as easy as it sounds. You must find a way to "go within" that is comfortable for you, whether it is in quiet contemplation, prayer, or meditation. Listen to the stillness and get in touch with your feelings. Or perhaps talk to a trusted friend, keeping the conversation positive and constructive. Remember that a loving attitude toward yourself, others, and God is the most positive building block upon which to base your life.

Another important ingredient in relaxation is to find time to bring a sense of peace into your life. It may take the form of a good novel, a half-hour of meditation, or a leisurely walk through the park. Although exercise is a form of relaxation, it should not be your only time "away from it all." Take a peaceful, mental break on a regular basis.

Chapter 4

COSMETIC CUISINE

The following Cayce reading emphasizes the proper role of cosmetics in skin care: "Don't depend upon cosmetics to clear or purify the skin. The cosmetics should be rather as an aid to keeping the superficial circulation in portions of face and hands in bettered conditions." (Edgar Cayce reading 5271-1)

There are as many cosmetic products on the market today as there are prepackaged microwave foods. Finding your way through the labyrinth of the skin and hair care section of your drug- or health food store can be as difficult as locating healthy foods in the maze of time-saving concoctions in the freezer section.

As we've discussed, the beauty of Cayce's approach to radiant hair and skin is the stress he placed on promoting beauty within—not only by balancing vital body systems but also by maintaining positive, loving attitudes. Yet there's an additional plus to the readings that shouldn't go unnoticed.

Cayce also gave simple, basic advice for the external care of the skin which can complement your body's inner working.

GUARD AGAINST ENEMIES

This is the first rule and the most important. Sun, wind, cold, and chemicals are your skin's natural enemies. Guard against them, and your skin will be your lifelong friend.

Think for a moment of the effects the sun can have on carpet or upholstery which is exposed to the bright sun through a window or doorway. One year of too much direct exposure can fade and dry rot a heavy duty fabric. What, then, does the sun do to your skin? Now, contemplate the effects of wind, rain, and cold on an outdoor paint job? Peeling, cracking paint is not a pretty sight, nor is peeling, cracking skin (and it's painful, too!). Finally, think of the effects of scouring powder on a dirty tub. What is it doing to your skin?

STAY OUT OF THE ELEMENTS

Cayce specifically indicated to stay out of the sun between 11:00 a.m. and 2:00 p.m., when the sun's rays are at their peak. Not only does the sun potentially burn (and thus destroy) the outer layer of your skin, but it also has an adverse effect on the superficial circulation—which is vital to the nourishment of your skin. Likewise, wind and cold can dry, chap, and damage your skin in much the same way as the sun. So bundle up when you go outdoors in the winter; dress in full gear, including hat, scarf, and gloves. Also keep your face moisturized with one of the lotions to be discussed later.

BE CHEMICALLY INDEPENDENT

There's a long list of chemicals you may regularly encounter as you clean, scrub, and make repairs around the house. From dishwashing liquids, laundry detergents, and ammonia to turpentine and paint, there are plenty of chemical hazards within the walls of your own home and garage. The trick is to ensure that they don't come in direct contact with your skin. Your best bet is to wear cloth-lined rubber gloves, slipped on after you've rubbed your hands with a small amount of peanut oil. Be sure not to wear them for a prolonged period of time and dispose of them if the lining itself comes in contact with the chemical.

SIMPLE SOAP AND WATER

The readings recommended several different types of soap but most often recommended Castile soap, which has an olive oil base. Black and White soaps and products were also frequently recommended because of their alkaline nature. Your health food store and many drugstores carrying natural products will have some of these soaps. It's best that you test several and determine which one seems best for your own skin.

The water temperature, when you are washing, should be tepid—not hot and not cold. Use your fingertips to wash your face, using circular, upward motions. Downward strokes can pull at the connective tissues between the skin, bone, and muscles, which can result in sagging, drooping skin. Be especially careful around the eyes. When finished, rinse with warm water—not hot—and pat dry with a soft, cotton towel.

How often should you wash your face? A thorough cleansing in the morning and evening should be plenty. If you suffer from dry skin, consider simply rinsing your face in the morning, thus leaving intact the natural oils which your skin produced during the night.

AFTER CLEANING UP, MUD DOWN

If you have never treated yourself to a mud pack, I suggest you seriously consider rectifying that oversight. Cayce often recommended mud packs, preferably with Boncilla mud (which has a high chalk content) as the main ingredient. Though it will be difficult to locate a facial mask with Boncilla or chalk as an ingredient, there are several packs on the market with French green clay as a main ingredient. These are helpful and soothing.

Apply the damp mud to the face, using upward motions. As it dries, it serves as an astringent to shrink pores and tighten skin. This tightening action also increases circulation to the area. Once the mud has dried, usually in 15 minutes, rinse your face with tepid water and gently pat it dry.

In applying a mud pack the Cayce readings also urged that the applications extend to the neck and throat, covering the area over the thyroid. The readings recommended treating yourself to this facial therapy once or even twice monthly. Regarding this advice I would recommend that you take your skin type into consideration. If your skin tends toward dryness, then lean toward less frequent applications.

Follow this facial treatment with the Peanut Oil Lotion described in the next section.

SMOOTHING THINGS OVER

The Cayce readings offer several suggestions for natural skin lotions, fresheners, and cleansers.

PEANUT OIL LOTION

Once or twice a week take the time to bathe in a warm bath for fifteen to twenty minutes, washing with a mild, olive oil-based soap. After bathing, massage your body with the following lotion, beginning with the face and neck, then shoulders and arms, and downward on the torso. Pay particular attention to the diaphragm area, and across the waist and hips. Completely massage the legs, knees, ankles, and feet.

To make this lotion, begin with peanut oil as the base and add the ingredients which follow in the order listed:

Peanut oil	6 oz.
Olive oil	2 oz.
Rose water	2 oz.
Lanolin, dissolved	1 tbsp.

This massage routine will result in healthy, glowing skin along with an added plus: The readings also indicated that peanut oil, massaged regularly into the joints, would help prevent arthritis.

OLIVE OIL SKIN FRESHENER

One skin freshener recommended in the readings is this olive oil-based moisturizer which is prepared by combining the following:

Olive oil	½ pint
Rose water	1 oz.
Glycerine	3 drops
10% solution of alcohol	1 oz.

(10% grain alcohol to 90% distilled water)

The readings indicated that this lotion would have an invigorating effect upon the skin.

COCOA BUTTER CLEANSER

Here's a cleanser the readings stated would not only enliven the skin and the circulation, but also cleanse the skin.

Melt the cocoa butter, then add to it these ingredients:

Melted cocoa butter   1 tbsp.

Rose water   1 tbsp.

Compound tincture of benzoin   1 tbsp.

THE UNDERARM ENEMY

The readings' recommendation regarding anti-perspirants was simple and straightforward: Don't use them. Washing the underarms thoroughly with a mild soap was the favored alternative. Reality may dictate, however, the use of some form of deodorant which does not clog the pores, but which does deodorize by checking the action of the bacteria which cause the unfavorable odor. Since the readings' primary caution was against any preparation that "closes the pores of the skin to prevent perspiration" (Edgar Cayce reading 2072-6), use of a natural deodorant is not necessarily in conflict with the readings. Check your local health food store which may carry cosmetic products. You'll probably find several natural deodorants from which to choose.

TO MAKE UP OR BREAK OUT?

"Each body should rather prefer to be natural than using any makeup . . . " (Edgar Cayce reading 308-2) This readings quote seems clear enough. Once you begin a program which promotes beauty from within and you switch to natural lotions and cleansers, your skin should begin to radiate with health. Dark circles under your eyes, which are the result of toxic build-up and lack of rest, should begin to disappear as your program progresses.

One difference between Cayce's time and the present is the availability of natural facial cosmetics. If you absolutely feel the need for some makeup when heading to the office or for attending a special event, use only a minimum application, and do this as infrequently as possible. How can you select the right products? Where do you find them?

The key is to find natural products which, like the deodorants discussed above, do not clog the pores and irritate the skin. Many natural product lines are now available through independent distributors, health food stores, or in some department stores. Your best approach is to find a basic line of makeup which you find agrees with your skin and then stay with it.

WHEN TO SHAMPOO AND HOW

The readings imply that there are two purposes for shampooing. The first is to cleanse the hair and scalp, the second is to stimulate circulation in the scalp. It is generally accepted that you should shampoo as often as your hair seems to require it. Be sure, however, not to wait too long between washes, for though the hair may seem clean, the scalp might be suffering from a build-up of dying skin which can clog your pores.

Olive oil shampoo is the most frequently suggested type of hair cleanser in the readings. A Castile shampoo is similar and also recommended. Your health food store should have a variety of these kinds of shampoos from which to choose.

To wash your hair properly, wet it thoroughly beforehand. Spread the shampoo in the palms of your hands, then gently lather your hair. To massage your scalp, rub it in a circular motion, actually moving the skin over the skull, as opposed to simply rubbing the top of the scalp. Continue massaging for ten minutes. This motion will stimulate the circulation, which nourishes hair follicles. Afterwards, rinse thoroughly and completely.

Chapter 5

REMEDIES FOR HEALTHY SKIN AND HAIR

The Cayce readings were rich in suggested remedies for common skin and hair ailments, from unsightly and persistent warts to periodic outbreaks of poison ivy. Many of the suggested therapies are simple, such as castor oil for the removal of moles. Others are more complex, such as a detailed regimen for the treatment of acne.

There is a common ingredient in all remedies, however, that should be the building block of any therapy. You must *believe* that the therapy will be successful, that it will assist your body's natural healing powers to bring about a balanced, healthy condition.

As you use the following remedies throughout the years, always begin with a positive outlook and a belief that healing will come. These mental attitudes will put you on the road to recovery. Without them, the road may take unexpected turns before healing occurs.

ACNE

The acne pimple is a teenager's most feared skin complaint. As we all know, these unsightly bumps can appear sporadically throughout one's adult years as well.

A pimple is an oil gland duct which has become plugged but continues to secrete sebum. Pressure builds up within the gland and eventually erupts, emptying irritating sebum into the dermis. The immune system responds immediately. White cells rush to the area on a wave of healing blood, causing the telltale swelling and redness we know so well.

What causes the oil gland to plug up? The Cayce readings pinpointed an imbalance in the elimination and circulation systems as the primary culprit. Since acne is a serious skin problem and is persistent in nature, therapy involves several processes which should be consistently followed.

Improve Your Eliminations   Refer to Chapter 2 for general guidelines to help you understand how to maintain an effective eliminations system. In the case of acne, drinking plenty of water is a must.

Consider, however, additional measures, such as taking a mild laxative like Eno salts. Take one teaspoonful each morning for five mornings, then leave off for five days, and then begin again. Continue this for three or four series and monitor your results.

Here's an odd suggestion but one which was mentioned frequently in the readings. To aid the kidneys and bladder in the elimination process, obtain some plain Coca-cola syrup (which is a natural diuretic) from a health food store. Take a teaspoon of this syrup mixed in a glass of plain water three times a week.

Consult with Your Osteopath or Chiropractor The focus of the adjustments should be to aid the coordination of the superficial and deeper circulation which is often disturbed in people suffering from acne problems.

Wash Twice a Day Bathe the affected area thoroughly twice a day with a natural Castile soap or genuine Black and White soap.

Control Your Diet Eat a diet which consists primarily of vegetables, with small quantities of fish, fowl, and lamb. Avoid all fried foods; carbonated drinks, sweets, pork, and red meat. Limit starches to one per meal.

Two Almonds a Day One reading suggested eating two almonds a day to avoid blemishes. This simple suggestion is certainly worth a try!

Acne Lotion The first step in making this lotion is to add camphor to olive oil. Do this by heating four ounces of olive oil, then add one ounce of natural camphor crystals (add cautiously so as not to spatter the mixture and burn yourself).

Then, combine the following ingredients in the order given:

Camphorated olive oil	2 oz.
Witch hazel	1 oz.
Russian White Oil	1 oz.

Shake this lotion well (it will separate while on the shelf) and massage into the skin twice a day.

Many may find it odd that an oil-based substance is suggested to combat acne. But such therapy makes sense.

The massaging of the skin with a camphorated oil mixture will stimulate the circulation—which will, in turn, assist in the breakup and elimination of toxins in the system. Remember, Cayce pinpointed poor circulation and poor elimination as major culprits in the creation of acne.

ATHLETE'S FOOT

Athlete's foot is much more than a little germ lurking in the locker room. According to Cayce, poor eliminations and poor circulation to the lower limbs contribute to the life of this fungal infection.

If you suspect "athlete's foot" is the cause of your discomfort, the readings gave some helpful advice.

Consult with Your Osteopath or Chiropractor Visit your osteopath or chiropractor to obtain treatments that will eliminate any disturbances of the nervous system and the circulatory system, particularly as they function throughout the lower extremities.

Improve Your Eliminations Be mindful of the advice in Chapter 2 regarding your eliminations and supplement your efforts with an evening drink of Mullein tea, which will improve the removal of toxins from the system.

Watch Your Diet Be sure to adhere strictly to the alkaline-reacting diet as described in Chapter 2. A refinement to that diet, however, which will help you improve your athlete's foot condition, is to concentrate more on vegetables and eat fewer fruits and legumes.

FOOT RUB

The following special oil rub was also recommended:

Russian White Oil	1 oz.
Witch hazel	1 oz.
Sassafras oil	1 oz.
Pure kerosene	1 oz.

Begin by measuring out the Russian White Oil and then add the next three ingredients. Shake the mixture well and massage into the feet and ankles.

BLACKHEADS

Blackheads are plugs of dried oil which form in the skin's pores. As with acne, Cayce stressed the importance of keeping the elimination and circulation properly balanced to help prevent and correct blackheads. Chapter 2 offers guidelines for accomplishing these ends. Additionally, the following simple and safe therapy for the removal of blackheads was recommended:

Apply a warm Turkish towel (not hot, not steaming) to the affected area and leave on for approximately eight to ten minutes. Afterwards, rub your face thoroughly with pure Castile soap. Follow this with cold cloths for one or two minutes, until you've applied them three or four times. Then, pat the area firmly and vigorously until circulation to the area has been restored. Do not use any creams or face powders after this application because this might add to the blockage of the pores.

CALLUSES, CORNS, AND BUNIONS

According to the readings, these painful sores are the result of eliminations being thrown out in improper directions. The following therapy was prescribed:

Prepare a paste of baking soda or bicarbonate of soda, dampened with spirits of camphor. Bathe your leg from the knee down with olive oil. Then, massage the paste into the area for three to five minutes and cover with a thin, light cloth overnight. You will probably experience sharp little sensations and soreness in the area even after several subsequent applications. But after five to ten days of applications or when the soreness has gone away, use equal parts of olive oil (1 tbsp.) and tincture of myrrh (1 tbsp.) as a massage compound on the area until the skin looks smooth and healed. Heat the oil first, then carefully add the myrrh. Make only enough for one application.

DANDRUFF

The Cayce readings targeted poor circulation as a major cause of dry, flaking scalp. You'll find any of these remedies helpful for this embarrassing and persistent condition:

OIL OF PINE HAIR TONIC

Combine the following ingredients in the order given:

Spring water	4 oz.
85% solution of grain alcohol	20 drops
(85% grain alcohol diluted with 15% spring water)	
Oil of pine	2 drops

Rub this tonic completely into the scalp until it has been thoroughly treated. When massaging the scalp, be sure to actually move the skin in circular motions, as though you are loosening it from the bone. Then, while the hair is still damp from the application, massage a very small quantity of white Vaseline into the scalp, again thoroughly and completely. Follow this by a shampoo with Pine Tar Soap (check your local health food store).

Follow this routine once a week and continue until the condition improves.

LISTERINE AND GLYCO-THYMOLINE RINSE

After shampooing with an olive oil-based shampoo, rinse with Listerine. Following your next shampooing, rinse with Glyco-Thymoline. Continue this cycle until the condition is eradicated.

What could possibly be the rationale for this therapy? It's simple. Listerine is acid in nature, Glyco-Thymoline alkaline. The cyclic treatment with these rinses will help balance the pH of the scalp and thus restore it to a healthier condition.

TAR SOAP SHAMPOO AND VASELINE

Once a week wash and massage the scalp with pure tar soap. Afterwards, massage a small amount of white Vaseline into the scalp for conditioning. Let this take effect at least overnight before washing it out with an olive oil-based shampoo.

DRY SKIN

We all know what dry skin is and how it feels. One suggestion made in the Cayce readings stands out above all the others: apply peanut oil as a lotion to the area. Should there be continued irritation or a prickling sensation from the oil, add ½ to 1 teaspoonful of dissolved lanolin to the oil.

A special exercise was given for those people with dry hands and skin. The readings indicated that it would aid the body in assimilation by stimulating the gastric flow. Although this exercise was described in Chapter 3, it warrants being repeated here.

Stretch the arms above the head and reach as high as you can or, even better, grab hold of a bar or other structure that you can safely swing from (the readings suggested a tree limb!). Hold on, relaxing your body, not your grip! Stretch or swing like this until you feel the tension leave your body. Repeat this regularly, once or twice a day. It will aid the body in digestion and assimilation.

FEET—DRY AND PEELING

If your feet are dry and peeling but a fungal infection (such as athlete's foot) is not suspected, it is likely that poor circulation is one probable culprit. Massage deeply and regularly with equal parts of olive oil and peanut oil. Consider asking your chiropractor or osteopath to make a helpful adjustment which will aid circulation in the lower extremities.

GRAYING HAIR

Among the suspected causes of graying hair are stress, poor diet, and poor circulation in the scalp. To maintain healthy hair and to prevent graying, Cayce recommended eating the skins of Irish potatoes prepared in one of two ways. First, you can steam the skins in Patapar paper (available in health food stores) or you can prepare a juice from the skins by stewing them in a little water and drinking the juice.

In both preparations it is stressed not to eat the meat of the potato, but just the skins.

MOLES

The readings did not always encourage the removal of moles, those dark spots which we sometimes think are unsightly. However, they did offer a simple suggestion for their removal if this was so desired: To massage the area—on the mole and around it—with castor oil, twice a day. Continue the treatment until the spot goes away.

NAILS

Proper care of nails requires vigilance in diet, eliminations, and circulation. In the diet arena, adequate quantities of calcium were stressed. As mentioned earlier, foods rich in calcium include sunflower seeds, cheese, milk, and green vegetables. A good practice is to have a green salad for lunch, sprinkled with sunflower seeds and gelatin.

Cayce also indicated that the thyroid affects the health of nails. Refer to "Thyroid Therapy" in Chapter 3 and be sure to include these practices in your health regimen.

Finally, the readings recommended two different massage compounds for nails and cuticles. The first is simply a drop or two of Atomidine rubbed gently on and around the nail. Although this will tend to color the nail at first, it will also strengthen and prevent its breaking. The second compound was a paste of pure apple cider vinegar and table salt applied in the same way. Choose the one which seems to work for you.

POISON IVY

Anyone who has had poison ivy knows how maddening the persistent itch can be. The readings recommended Atomidine as a remedy taken in the following manner: one to two drops in half a glass of water in the morning for four to five days. Then discontinue.

In addition, prepare a weakened solution of Atomidine—one teaspoonful to half a glass of water—and sponge off the infected area. This is soothing and will help dry up the rash.

As is the admonition for almost all skin disorders, take a good eliminant. This will help flush the system of poisons which, because of disturbances from the rash, will accumulate in the superficial circulation. Eno salts is a recommended remedy. Take one teaspoonful in a glass of water daily for eight to ten days during the itchy siege.

SCARS

For cutaneous scars or healed wounds the Cayce readings suggest several different scar massage formulas which have as a common ingredient camphorated oil.

The first step in making this lotion is to add camphor to olive oil in the following manner: Heat four ounces of olive oil, then add one ounce of natural camphor crystals (add it cautiously so as not to spatter and burn yourself).

SCAR MASSAGE FORMULA

Mix the following ingredients to create the classic scar massage formula:

Camphor added to olive oil	2 oz.
Lanolin, dissolved	½ tsp.
Peanut oil	1 oz.

Using your fingertips, gently massage this formula into your scar once or twice daily for five minutes.

OLIVE OIL AND TINCTURE OF MYRRH FORMULA

You might like to experiment with alternating the Scar Massage Formula with the compound of olive oil and tincture of myrrh.

Heat 1 tbsp. of olive oil and carefully add 1 tbsp. of myrrh. Make only enough for one application. Adjust the above measurements (always equal amounts) according to your needs, which will be dictated by the size of your scar.

Enlist Mind Power   The following Cayce reading is a particularly beautiful and insightful one. It represents important element from the Cayce philosophy—that healing is most effective if it first occurs on the spiritual level.

> "Let the scars be removed from . . . the *own mental and spiritual self.* Turn to those things of making application of the fruits of the spirit of truth; love, patience, gentleness, kindness, long-suffering, brotherly love, putting away those little tendencies for being 'catty' at times or being selfish or expressing jealousy and such.
>
> "Let that mind be in thee as was in Him, who is the way and the truth and the light, and He will make the light of love so shine through thy countenance that few, if any, will ever see the scars made by self-indulgence in other experiences."
>
> (Edgar Cayce reading 5092-1)

SUNBURN

Sunburn results when overexposure to the sun's harsh rays causes a number of changes, including an extreme dilation of the skin's blood vessels. Hence, the redness and burning sensation occur. The readings specifically advised staying out of the sun between 11 a.m. and 2 p.m.

Cayce offered several remedies for sunburn.

Don't Press Your Luck   First and foremost, do not stay out in the sun. If you burn, whether you're on vacation or not, do not expose your skin to further damage. This is common sense—but unfortunately not common practice until the burn is so severe that the sun becomes unbearable.

Pure Apple Cider Vinegar   After taking a lukewarm bath, rub your body down with plain, pure apple cider vinegar. This natural remedy will help soothe the pain of the burn.

Glyco-Thymoline   Apply pure Glyco-Thymoline to the burned areas for relief of pain.

Vaseline   If rough spots appear as a result of a burn, wash the area with a mild soap and then apply Vaseline to the affected area. Repeat until the condition is improved.

Spirits of Camphor   In the event that there is a more acute rash or outbreak, apply spirits of camphor directly to the area with a sterile cotton ball. Wait an hour or two, then take a tepid bath, followed by a rubdown with pure peanut oil.

WARTS

Medical science contends that warts are caused by a virus and can be transmitted either to other people or to other parts of the host's body. They occur most frequently on the hands, arms, and legs. Children are particularly susceptible to these unsightly bumps.

While Cayce was not in disagreement with medical science's theory, he did pinpoint other sources for warts.

On the one hand, he indicated that they were the result of eliminations being thrown off from the body through improper channels, the small tumor or wart being the result.

On the other hand, they are more common in young people between the ages of ten and twenty because of the glandular changes happening during puberty. During the time period of these changes, the cellular forces of the body are in transition, and warts can result.

Cayce offered several remedies for warts, ranging from hypnotic suggestion to a paste made of castor oil and baking soda. Of the many Cayce remedies people have tested over the years, these recommendations for warts have been among the most often reported as being successful.

Castor Oil   Apply castor oil to the wart twice a day, massaging it in thoroughly, gently, and persistently.

Castor Oil and Baking Soda   Prepare a paste of castor oil and baking soda. Apply this to the wart overnight, securing it with a loose bandage or Band-Aid. Do this until the wart disappears.

20% Solution of Hydrochloric Acid   Using a small glass rod or broom straw, place a drop of the solution on the bump. Do this daily. As the wart begins to discolor, do not pick at it, for this may result in infection. Rather, let the wart "wear off" with time.

Power of Suggestion   The best way to incorporate Cayce's recommendation to use suggestion to treat an unsightly wart is to visualize its disappearance while persistently applying any of the above remedies. Belief that the remedy you choose will work is vital to its success.

WRINKLES AND SAGGING

To avoid wrinkles, Cayce suggested massage and the use of the Peanut Oil Lotion around the eyes, the chin, and the throat. Application of mud packs was also mentioned as a deterrent because of the tightening effect it has on the skin. For under-eye wrinkles Cayce suggested applying pure castor oil and leaving it on overnight. Also, proper rest and a relaxed, smiling face will work wonders!

Chapter 6

BATTLING BALDNESS

Hair. The crowning glory of one's youth sometime becomes a source of embarrassment in later years. Mos men and women are faced with hair loss of one degree o another at some point in their lives. Whether it be th threat of severe baldness or simply thinning hai sufferers know that this condition is no laughing matte Many books and treatments offer miracle cures ar promises of restored hair loss. What the Cayce reading offer is a unique understanding of the problem and a ho of possible treatments. Upon examination of th readings, several common approaches to therapy emerg

ANATOMY OF HEALTHY HAIR

As we learned earlier, the hair root is found at th base of the follicle and is located in the dermis layer skin. Capillaries, which weave throughout the texture the dermis, deliver a crimson stream of nutrients to the ites. In each follicle is a sebaceous gland which produces oil to help condition and protect the hair. As your hair grows, it leaves behind cells which can be likened to seeds. If properly stimulated and nourished, these cells later form a new strand of hair when the old one falls out. Baldness and permanent loss of hair occurs when the hair follicles are clogged by dried oils or by a build-up of residue from hair-care products. Lack of circulation of nutrient-rich blood to nourish the follicle can also result in stunted hair growth.

Anatomy aside, let's get to the root of the problem. What actually causes hair loss? Can it be prevented? Can hair be actually restored?

THE ROOT OF THE PROBLEM

Spinal Misalignment In the 50 Cayce readings which dealt with hair loss the most frequent cause which emerged as a pattern was a misalignment of the spine. How can this cause hair loss? Let's review the role of the spine. Though we covered this information in more detail in Chapter 2, it's worth repeating the basics here.

The spine is the body's "nerve center." It acts as the distributing network for nerve impulses—which regulate the activities of the glands and organs, control blood supply, and nurture tissues throughout our body's universe. As we've learned earlier, proper functioning of glands, elimination organs, and circulation are vital to the health of skin and hair.

Thyroid Imbalance The second most frequently cited cause was an imbalance in the functioning of the thyroid. As mentioned earlier, the thyroid regulates

metabolism which interfaces with the nervous system
Hence, thyroid imbalance can have the same effects on
the body as a spinal misalignment. The energies
distributed throughout the body which promote balance
eliminations and circulation can "short ciruit" due to
disturbances in metabolism. This will cause toxic build-up
and sluggish circulation. The result in this instance
dried-up and undernourished hair follicles.

Debilitation Tied for third place (along with
toxemia and poor capillary circulation) as the most
frequently mentioned cause of baldness was
"debilitation" or "sapped vital energies." It is likely that
this term was the readings' way of labeling what we today
refer to as the arch enemy of health—stress. Stress has
debilitating effect on the balance of all body systems. In
Chapter 2 we noted the effects that negative emotion
can have on our bodies. Stress works in much the same
way. It creates a tenseness throughout our bodies and
according to Cayce, even causes poisons to be secreted by
the glands. Along with a multitude of other ill effects
these conditions will disturb circulation, elimination, and
assimilation.

Toxemia Toxemia (also tied in the race for third place
was mentioned as a significant cause of hair loss in several
readings. The readings emphasize, of course, that toxic
conditions throughout the body greatly disturb
circulation. Toxemia specifically refers to the build-up of
toxic substances in the blood, which can irritate
circulation and upset other bodily functions.

Poor Capillary Circulation Poor capillary circulation was also cited as an important factor in the baldness battle. And, of course, it makes sense. The capillary circulation interfaces directly with the hair follicles, bringing them nourishment and stimulation. The four causes of hair loss already discussed—spinal misalignment, thyroid imbalance, debilitation, and toxemia—all have in common an indirect effect on the red river of life that fertilizes the seeds of new hair.

PREVENTION

As with any undesired physical condition, prevention is by far the advised route over cure. Prevention, though not always easy in and of itself, is easier in comparison to its often stubborn alternative.

Based on the unique insights of the readings into the causes of hair loss, a potentially powerful preventative routine is possible.

CARE FOR YOUR SPINE

As we've stressed before, having a regular routine of massage and spinal adjustments is basic for good health. If you are particularly concerned about potential hair loss, settle into a weekly massage and biweekly adjustment routine. Talk with your massage therapist and osteopath or chiropractor about your concerns. Your massage therapist can concentrate on stimulating circulation in your neck and scalp. Ask her or him to pay particular attention to the thyroid to stimulate its activity through massage. In addition your osteopath or chiropractor can be sensitive to maintaining the health of your body's vital "circuit"—the spine.

REMEMBER THYROID THERAPY

In Chapter 2 you learned about several hints for a healthy thyroid. You should review them in detail. In summary, however, remember to include iodine-rich foods in your diet—seafood and kelp are the primary sources. Also, when applying facial lotions or mud packs, be sure to extend them around your neck and over the thyroid area at the base of the throat. Finally follow the standard Atomidine routine, also described in Chapter 2, as a preventative measure.

WARD OFF THE RAVAGES OF STRESS

Diet, exercise, and relaxation—these are the blocks upon which to build your natural defenses against the ravages of general debilitation and stress. Follow the guidelines for these three activities found in Chapter 2.

It's important to emphasize at this point, however, the head and neck exercise on page 24. This exercise was specifically mentioned in relation to hair loss. One of the benefits of this routine is to relax muscles and stimulate circulation to the head. Do this exercise at least three times a day if you are combating hair loss.

CLEAN UP YOUR ACT

Along with the many sources of toxins in our bodies—from the wastes produced in the digestive process to dead and dying cells which must be washed away—there are several other toxic substances which are a part of many life styles. Smoking, alcohol, caffeine, and processed foods all have a toxic effect and disturb our body processes. If you are under siege by a balding scalp, elimination of or at least moderation with these substances is greatly advised.

GET OUT AND CIRCULATE

Keep moving. An active life style that includes exercise and stretching, fresh air, and an occasional light sweat will do wonders to keep the heart pump strong and provide stimulation for the lymph system as well. Design a regular exercise program as suggested in Chapter 2. The end result will be a fitter body, a quieter mind, and a more peaceful soul. Not only will you feel better, but your scalp will start to tingle and be invigorated from the increased circulatory activity *and* the reduced toxic build-up.

SCALP AND HAIR MASSAGE

There's a special technique to use when massaging your scalp. Place your fingertips on both sides of your scalp and literally move the scalp up and around in a circular motion. This will help loosen the skin from the skull—giving it room to breathe. Circulation will be increased and your hair follicles will receive a steadier stream of much needed nutrients from the superficial circulatory system.

NO SURE CURES—BUT HOPE AT LAST!

The following 34-day cycle of treatment was recommended to a 26-year-old male, Mr. [4056], who had begun to lose his hair in his late teens. His questions to Edgar Cayce were specifically about his problem with hair loss. The reading Cayce gave recommended a conservative treatment plan combining diet, thyroid therapy, and specific scalp treatments. Although the young man who was given this advice did not report back regarding the results, the treatment program was used years later by a young man who found it to be successful.

Supplement this cycle with a well-rounded "healthy hair" life style that includes proper diet, balanced eliminations, general attention to circulation through the body, and rest and relaxation. Review the advice in Chapter 2 and incorporate it into your daily routine and you'll be positioned for positive results.

34-DAY CYCLE

Days 1 through 5. Atomidine Routine. Take one drop of Atomidine in half a glass of water in the morning before breakfast.

Days 6 through 10. Scalp Treatment. Apply crude oil for 10 to 15 minutes with an electric vibrator that has a suction applicator. Afterwards, rinse with a solution of 20% grain alcohol to 80% spring water. Then apply a small amount of white Vaseline to the scalp and massage it in with an electric suction vibrator for another 10 to 15 minutes. Thoroughly cover the scalp and allow the

Vaseline to remain overnight. In the morning wash gently with an olive oil-based shampoo or tar soap.

Days 11 through 15. Repeat *Atomidine Routine.*

Days 16 through 20. Repeat *Scalp Treatment.*

Days 21 through 34. Special Diet Focus. Eat a diet that is rich in iodine in its natural form. Use kelp salt or sea salt rather than iodized salt. Consume plenty of seafood. Eat a raw lunch. Include the skin of Irish potatoes, either steamed or stewed, as a part of your diet three to four times a week.

Also, avoid sweets. Eat egg yolks but not egg whites.

Discontinue this routine for two weeks and then repeat it.

The readings suggest that following this cycle for six to eight months, with two-week intervals in between, will result in renewed hair growth. Be consistent and persistent and, most of all, believe that it will work.

GOOD LUCK!

CONCLUSION

LET YOUR LIGHT SHINE

As you nurture your skin and hair, you'll see and feel your beauty magnifying more and more each day. Though you may take detours and run into temporary roadblocks, remember that you were born with an inner beauty and that it longs to be expressed. This refrain is heard again and again in the Cayce readings.

To benefit truly from the suggestions you've learned in this book, remember how important it is to desire beauty not for vanity's sake, but for the sake of adding a bit of beauty to the world in which you live. That's accomplished by more than just a glowing complexion and flowing hair, but also from a radiant smile and sparkling eyes. Wear these as regularly as you do your favorite clothes.

A final word from the Cayce readings will give you inspiration. "If we would have life, give it. If we would have love, make ourselves lovely. If we would have beauty within our lives, make our lives beautiful. If we would have beauty in body or mind, or soul, create that atmosphere . . . " (Edgar Cayce reading 2096-1)

APPENDIX A

WHO WAS EDGAR CAYCE?

Edgar Cayce exhibited unusual psychic ability at an early age and soon became known for his remarkable clairvoyant gifts. In a self-induced state, he was able to diagnose illnesses and prescribe remedies with remarkable success. Often referred to as "the sleeping prophet" and the world's most documented psychic, Edgar Cayce left behind a legacy of over 14,000 psychic readings covering such subjects as healing, dreams, meditation, reincarnation, prophecy, and psychic ability.

Born in 1877 in Hopkinsville, Kentucky, he discovered by accident that he could absorb information on any particular subject merely by napping for a while on a book pertaining to that topic. At the age of fifteen he suffered an accident, and, while in a coma, instructed his astonished parents to prepare a poultice to be applied at the base of his brain. The application fully restored him.

After he reached adulthood, his job as a salesman was threatened by a mysterious paralysis of the throat muscles which medical doctors were unable to treat. He consulted a hypnotist, and it was under the subsequent trance that Edgar correctly diagnosed his condition and prescribed an almost immediate cure.

Not long after, Edgar discovered that his gift could be used to help others, and what followed was over forty years of helping people from his self-induced state of unconsciousness. For 22 of these years, his readings were largely confined to medical problems; however, the scope of Edgar's abilities expanded in later years to include such subjects as meditation, dreams, reincarnation, and the Bible.

Edgar Cayce is regarded today as one of the most significant explorers of the human psyche in the twentieth century.

APPENDIX B

HOW THE A.R.E. CAN HELP YOU

A wealth of information from the Edgar Cayce readings is available to you on hundreds of topics, from astrology and arthritis to universal laws and world affairs, through the organization which Edgar Cayce founded in 1931, the Association for Research and Enlightenment, Inc.

The facilities and benefits offered by the A.R.E. include the largest body of documented psychic information anywhere in the world: the 14,263 Cayce readings, copies of which are housed in the A.R.E. Library/Conference Center in Virginia Beach, Virginia. These readings have been indexed under 10,000 different topics and are currently being placed on computer. They are available to the public.

Membership in the A.R.E. is inexpensive and includes benefits such as: the bimonthly magazine, *Venture Inward;* home-study lessons in spiritual awareness and growth; the A.R.E. Library, available to you through book-borrowing by mail, offering collections of the actual Edgar Cayce readings as well as access to one of the world's best parapsychological book collections; and the names of doctors or health care professionals in your area who are willing to work with the remedies prescribed in the Edgar Cayce readings.

As an organization on the leading edge of exciting new fields of study, A.R.E. also presents seminars around the nation, led by prominent authorities in various fields and exploring such areas as parapsychology, dreams, meditation, personal growth, world religions, reincarnation and life after death, and holistic health.

The unique path to personal growth outlined in the Cayce readings is developed through a worldwide program of study groups. These informal groups meet weekly in private homes—right in your community—for friendly consciousness-expanding discussions.

A.R.E. maintains a visitors' center that offers a well-stocked bookstore, exhibits, classes, a movie, and audiovisual presentations to introduce seekers from all walks of life to the fascinating concepts found in the Cayce readings.

A.R.E. conducts ongoing research into the helpfulness of both the medical and nonmedical readings, often giving members the opportunity to participate in the studies themselves.

For more information and a free color brochure, write or phone:

A.R.E., P.O. Box 595
67th Street and Atlantic Avenue
Virginia Beach, VA 23451, (804) 428-3588

APPENDIX C

WHERE TO FIND THE REMEDIES AND INGREDIENTS

Some of the formulations mentioned in the Edgar Cayce readings are available from:

Home Health Products
P.O. Box 3130
Virginia Beach, VA 23451

APPENDIX D

DIRECTIONS FOR SELF-ADMINISTERED THERAPIES

ADMINISTERING AN ENEMA

Here are some basic guidelines for a home enema. First, gather the following items:

Enema bag	Two large towels
Vaseline	Plastic trash bag
Alcohol	Salt
Pure spring water	Glyco-Thymoline
	Sodium bicarbonate

Begin by sterilizing with alcohol the tube or nozzle attached to the enema bag. Prepare a quart of lukewarm spring water (98.6° F.), adding a teaspoon each of sodium bicarbonate and salt. Spread out a large plastic trash bag beneath several towels on the bed or floor and lie down on your left side. Have the bag elevated above the level of your body. Coat the enema nozzle with Vaseline and insert it two to four inches into your rectum. (Caution: do not force it.) Allow one third of the water to enter your colon slowly. If you begin to cramp, clamp the tube shut and take several deep breaths. Then continue. Once one third of the water is inside, turn over on your back and allow the next third to enter, following the same procedure. Finally, shift to your right side and empty the remaining fluid from the bag into your body.

Now, try to hold the solution for five to fifteen minutes, moving gently to swish the fluid around in the colon. This allows the fluid to soften and loosens the wastes. Your next stop is the bathroom, where you can now expel the water.

Rest a few moments, then repeat the process until the fluid which leaves your body is mostly clear. Administer a final round of water, adding a teaspoonful of Glyco-Thymoline (which you can find at your health food store) to the water (instead of the salt and soda) to serve as an antiseptic to the colon area.

HOW TO HOME STEAM

Here are the directions for setting up a homemade steam cabinet. Begin by gathering the following items:

Straight-backed wooden chair   Old sheet
Two towels   Thermometer
Hot plate   Pie rack
Pan of boiling water   Custard cup
Oil or ingredient for
steam additive

Find a straight-backed chair, preferably wooden, which will not be damaged by short-term heat and moisture. Drape the chair in towels so that you won't burn your body. Place a hot plate and pan of boiling water beneath the chair. Find an old sheet that you'll use as your "steam sheet" again and again. Cut a hole in the middle of the sheet large enough to fit your head through.

Just prior to your steam, drink three glasses of water. Now, undress and sit on the chair, draping the sheet around you like a tent. Be sure that the sheet does not come in contact with the hot plate. Wrap a towel around your neck to keep the steam from escaping.

For safety's sake, have a friend or family member nearby who can check on you and provide you with drinking water to keep your body fluids balanced and to increase perspiration. Be sure to check your pulse and temperature periodically. Your pulse rate should remain below 140 beats per minute and your temperature below 104° F.

When you have worked up a good sweat, stand up slowly, check to see that you're not feeling faint, and proceed to the bathroom. Take a cleansing shower, and afterwards rub your body firmly with peanut oil, massaging your muscles and joints with deep, even strokes.

SPECIAL ADDITIVE TO A GOOD STEAM

Now that you know how to prepare a home steam cabinet, I'd be amiss if I did not give you instructions on how to add special healing substances and oils to the steam process to aid in helping stimulate elimination.

Find a small ovenproof glass dish or ceramic container (like a custard cup) and add a teaspoon of your choice of healing ingredient (only one type at any given steam). Float this in the pan of boiling water or place it over the water on a pie rack. The substance will vaporize as a result of the heat and help stimulate the skin.

Common additives are Atomidine, witch hazel, pine oil, wintergreen, lavender, tincture of myrrh, benzoin, and eucalyptus oil.